A Canadian Counting Book

Out on the Prairie

Cora Taylor   Pat Stephens

Scholastic Canada Ltd.

Toronto New York London Auckland Sydney
Mexico City New Delhi Hong Kong Buenos Aires

The artwork for each picture was prepared using acrylic and gouache on Peterborough Hi-Art illustration board.

This book was designed in QuarkXPress, with type set in 18 point Tiffany.

Scholastic Canada Ltd.
175 Hillmount Road, Markham, Ontario L6C 1Z7, Canada

Scholastic Inc.
555 Broadway, New York, NY 10012, USA

Scholastic Australia Pty Limited
PO Box 579, Gosford, NSW 2250, Australia

Scholastic New Zealand Limited
Private Bag 94407, Greenmount, Auckland, New Zealand

Scholastic Ltd.
Villiers House, Clarendon Avenue, Leamington Spa,
Warwickshire CV32 5PR, UK

Library and Archives Canada Cataloguing in Publication
Taylor, Cora, 1936-
Out on the prairie : a Canadian counting book / Cora Taylor ;
illustrations by Pat Stephens.
An adaptation of the traditional song Over in the meadow.
ISBN 0-439-95779-6
1. Counting—Juvenile literature. 2. Prairie animals—Canada—
Juvenile literature. I. Stephens, Pat II. Title. III. Title: Over in the meadow.
QA113.T39 2005   j513.2'11   C2004-904932-1

6 5 4 3 2 1   Printed in Singapore   05 06 07 08

To two terrific grandchildren, the youngest of the lot:
Emily Thomas and Alexander Mogg.
And to four wonderful great-grandchildren:
Luc LaPlante, Taylor Vida, Aidan Vida and Rachel Vida.
And great-nephews: Christopher Grieve and Jonathan Lee Grieve.

— C. T.

To Caitlin.

— P. S.

Out on the prairie, in the warm spring sun,
Lived a mother antelope and her young fawn one.
"Leap!" said the mother. "I leap!" said the one,
And it leaped and it played in the warm spring sun.

Out on the prairie, with its sky so blue,
Lived an old mother badger and her little cubs two.
"Bask!" said the mother. "We bask!" said the two,
And they basked and they dozed 'neath the sky so blue.

Out on the prairie, where the clouds float free,
Lived a red-tailed hawk and her baby hawks three.
"Soar!" said the mother. "We soar!" said the three,
And they soared in the sky where the clouds float free.

Out on the prairie, by the river shore,
Lived a mother chorus frog and her tadpoles four.
"Swim!" said the mother. "We swim!" said the four,
And they wiggled and they swam in a pond by the shore.

Out on the prairie, where the swallows dive,
Lived a bright bank swallow and her brood of five.
"Swoop!" said the mother. "We swoop!" said the five,
And they swooped and they dove till the sky looked alive.

Out on the prairie, in a nest made of sticks,
Lived a mother meadowlark and her nestlings six.
"Tweet!" said the mother. "We tweet!" said the six,
And they sang "tweet-a-bow!" in their nest made of sticks.

Out on the prairie, on the plains so even,
Lived a proud gopher mum and her family of seven.
"Dig!" said the mother. "We dig!" said the seven,
And they dug and kept cool in the sand so even.

Out on the prairie, in a field by the gate,
Lived a mother prairie chicken and her little chicks eight.
"Scratch!" said the mother. "We scratch!" said the eight,
And they scratched and they pecked in the field by the gate.

Out on the prairie, 'neath a tangle of twine,
Lived a mother deer mouse and her babies nine.
"Squeak!" said the mother. "We squeak!" said the nine,
And they squeaked and they squirmed in their nest made of twine

Out on the prairie, in a cosy den,
Lived a mother coyote and her young pups ten.
"Sleep!" said the mother. "Yes, soon!" said the ten,
And they tumbled and they nuzzled in their cosy den.

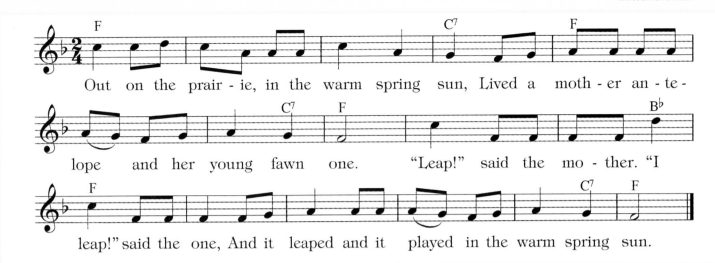

Out on the prair - ie, in the warm spring sun, Lived a moth - er an - te -

lope and her young fawn one. "Leap!" said the mo - ther. "I

leap!" said the one, And it leaped and it played in the warm spring sun.

All of the animals in this book are found on the Canadian prairie, a huge area of grassland and wetland stretching across parts of Manitoba, Saskatchewan and Alberta. Some of the land is flat, and some of it is gently rolling.

The prairie is home to many plants, animals, birds and insects, all of which depend on each other to survive.

1. The **pronghorn antelope** is the fastest land animal in North America. It eats a mixture of grasses, as well as leaves, flowers, twigs and bark.

2. The **North American badger** is a burrowing animal that has strong, sharp claws for digging.

3. The **red-tailed hawk** has a brownish-red tail, and wings that spread wide as it flies over open fields looking for food.

4. One of the tiniest frogs in Canada is the **boreal chorus frog**. It lives near water throughout the prairies and greets spring with a special song.

5. The **bank swallow** lives in large groups called colonies, and digs holes for its nests in the side of steep riverbanks.

6. The **Western meadowlark** loves wide-open spaces. Its joyful song is so loud, it can be heard from a great distance.

7. The **Richardson's ground squirrel** is more commonly known as the gopher. This rodent spends much of its life underground, in maze-like burrows full of twists and turns.

8. In Canada, **the sharp-tailed grouse** is often called the prairie chicken. A mother grouse digs a shallow hole and lines it with soft leaves and grasses to lay her eggs in.

9. The **prairie deer mouse** sleeps in its nest for most of the day, but comes out at night to feed on seeds, fruit and nuts.

10. The **coyote** is a relative of dogs and wolves. It is very smart, playful and a fast runner. When a coyote begins to howl at night, others often join in. No one knows why.